Microsoft® Word

2016

Workbook

Nita Rutkosky
Pierce College at Puyallup
Puyallup, Washington

Audrey Roggenkamp
Pierce College at Puyallup
Puyallup, Washington

Ian Rutkosky
Pierce College at Puyallup
Puyallup, Washington

PARADIGM
EDUCATION SOLUTIONS
St. Paul

Senior Vice President	Linda Hein
Editor in Chief	Christine Hurney
Director of Production	Timothy W. Larson
Production Editors	Rachel Kats, Jen Weaverling
Cover and Text Designer	Valerie King
Copy Editor	Sarah Kearin
Senior Design and Production Specialist	Jaana Bykonich
Assistant Developmental Editors	Mamie Clark, Katie Werdick
Testers	Desirec Carvel; Ann E. Mills, Ivy Tech Community College of Indiana, Indianapolis, IN
Instructional Support Writer	Brienna McWade
Indexer	Terry Casey
Vice President Information Technology	Chuck Bratton
Digital Projects Manager	Tom Modl
Vice President Sales and Marketing	Scott Burns
Director of Marketing	Lara Weber McLellan

Care has been taken to verify the accuracy of information presented in this book. However, the authors, editors, and publisher cannot accept responsibility for Web, email, newsgroup, or chat room subject matter or content, or for consequences from application of the information in this book, and make no warranty, expressed or implied, with respect to its content.

Trademarks: Microsoft is a trademark or registered trademark of Microsoft Corporation in the United States and/or other countries. Some of the product names and company names included in this book have been used for identification purposes only and may be trademarks or registered trade names of their respective manufacturers and sellers. The authors, editors, and publisher disclaim any affiliation, association, or connection with, or sponsorship or endorsement by, such owners.

Cover Photo Credits: © whitehoune/Shutterstock.com; © Mila Supinskaya/Shutterstock.com.

We have made every effort to trace the ownership of all copyrighted material and to secure permission from copyright holders. In the event of any question arising as to the use of any material, we will be pleased to make the necessary corrections in future printings. Thanks are due to the aforementioned authors, publishers, and agents for permission to use the materials indicated.

ISBN: 978-0-76387-137-6 (print)
ISBN: 978-0-76386-700-3 (digital)

© 2017 by Paradigm Publishing, Inc.
875 Montreal Way
St. Paul, MN 55102
Email: educate@emcp.com
Website: ParadigmCollege.com

Printed in the United States of America

24 23 22 21 20 19 18 17 16   1 2 3 4 5 6 7 8 9 10 11 12

Microsoft® Word

Study Tools

Study tools include a presentation and In Brief step lists. Use these resources to help you further develop and review skills learned in this section.

Knowledge Check

SNAP Check your understanding by identifying application tools used in this section. If you are a SNAP user, launch the Knowledge Check from your Assignments page.

Recheck

SNAP Check your understanding by taking this quiz. If you are a SNAP user, launch the Recheck from your Assignments page.

Skills Exercise

SNAP Additional activities are available to SNAP users. If you are a SNAP user, access these activities from your Assignments page.

Skills Review

Review 1   Editing a Hawaiian Specials Document

Data File

1. Open **FCTHawaiianSpecials.docx** and then save it with the name **1-FCTHawaiianSpecials**.
2. Insert the word *spectacular* between the words *the* and *Pacific* in the first sentence below the *White Sands Charters* heading.
3. Move the insertion point to the beginning of the paragraph below the *Air Adventures* heading and then type the sentence Experience beautiful coastlines and magnificent waterfalls, and fly inside an active volcano.
4. Select and then delete the words *Depending on weather, marine conditions, and access, your* located in the third sentence in the paragraph below the *White Sands Charters* heading.
5. Capitalize the *g* in *guides*. (This word now begins the sentence.)
6. Select and then delete the last sentence in the *Air Adventures* section (the sentence that begins *View untouched areas from*).
7. Undo the deletion and then redo the deletion.
8. Move the insertion point to the beginning of the document and then complete a spelling and grammar check on the document. (*Molokini* is spelled correctly.)

9. Use Thesaurus to change *delightful* in the paragraph in the *White Sands Charter* section to *enchanting*.
10. Save **1-FCTHawaiianSpecials.docx**.

Review 2 Creating and Using an AutoCorrect Entry

1. With **1-FCTHawaiianSpecials.docx** open, display the AutoCorrect dialog box, type HA in the *Replace* text box, type Hawaiian in the *With* text box, click the Add button, and then close the dialog box. Close the Word Options dialog box.
2. Move the insertion point to the end of the document and then type the text shown in Figure WB-1.1.
3. Delete the HA AutoCorrect entry at the AutoCorrect dialog box.

Figure WB-1.1 Review 2, Step 2

Luau Legends

Enjoy a spectacular HA dinner show featuring lavish prime rib and authentic HA buffet. This uniquely HA experience includes a traditional lei greeting, exceptional food and beverages, magic music of the islands, and Hawaii's finest performers. Join us each evening beginning at 7:30 p.m. for an evening of delicious HA food and spectacular performances.

4. Save, print, and then close **1-FCTHawaiianSpecials.docx**.

Review 3 Editing an Agreement

Data File

1. Open **WEIncentiveAgt.docx** and then save it with the name **1-WEIncentiveAgt**.
2. Complete a spelling and grammar check on the document.
3. Search for all occurrences of *Employee* and replace them with *Carol Shepard*.
4. Search for all occurrences of *Company* and replace them with *Worldwide Enterprises*.
5. Save, print, and then close **1-WEIncentiveAgt.docx**.

Review 4 Preparing a Fax Sheet

1. Click the File tab and then click the *New* option.
2. At the New backstage area, click in the search text box, type equity fax, and then press the Enter key.
3. Click the *Fax (Equity theme)* template and then click the Create button.
4. Insert the following information in the specified location:

- To: Scott Drysdale
- From: (Type your first and last names.)
- Fax: (213) 555-3349
- Pages: 3

- Phone: (213) 555-3400
- Date: (Insert current date.)
- Re: Incentive Agreement
- CC: (Delete this placeholder.)

Insert a capital *X* in the *Please Reply* check box. Click the *[Type comments]* placeholder and then type the following comment: Please review the Incentive Agreement and then call me so we can schedule an appointment.
5. Save the document with the name **1-WEAgtFax**.
6. Print and then close the document.

Skills Assessment

Assessment 1 Editing a Letter

1. Open **PTMarqueeLtr.docx** and then save it with the name **1-PTMarqueeLtr**.
2. Move the insertion point a double space below the paragraph of text in the letter and then add the following information. (Write the information as a paragraph—do not use bullets.)
   - Costume research takes approximately two to three weeks.
   - If appropriate costumes cannot be found, costumes are sewn.
   - Anticipate five working days to sew a costume.
   - Include the number of costumes and approximate sizes.
   - A price estimate will be provided before costumes are purchased or sewn.
3. Use Thesaurus to replace *regarding* in the first sentence with an appropriate synonym.
4. Save, print, and then close **1-PTMarqueeLtr.docx**.

Assessment 2 Writing a Letter

1. Display the New backstage area, search for and download the Business letter (Median theme) template, and then use the following information to create the letter. (You determine the salutation and closing.)

Sender's information:	Recipient's information:
The Waterfront Bistro	Marquee Productions
3104 Rivermist Drive	Mr. Josh Hart, Locations Director
Buffalo, NY 14280	955 South Alameda Street
	Los Angeles, CA 90037

2. Write a letter as Dana Hirsch that covers the following points. (Write the information in paragraphs—do not use bullets.)
   - Explain that The Waterfront Bistro is a full-service catering company with a number of menus for breakfast, lunch, dinner, and morning and afternoon snacks. Include the price ranges for breakfast, lunch, dinner, and snack menus. (You determine the ranges.)
   - Offer a 5% discount if you cater for the duration of the filming.
   - Tell Mr. Hart that you would like to fax a variety of menu options to him.
   - Close the letter by telling him you are very interested in his business and say something positive about your catering service.
3. Save the completed letter document with the name **1-WBCateringLtr**.
4. Print and then close the document.

Assessment 3 Preparing a Fax

1. Display the New backstage area, search for and download the Fax (Equity theme) template, and then insert the necessary information in the specified fields. You are Dana Hirsch and you are sending the fax to Josh Hart (see information in Assessment 2). His fax number is (612) 555-2009 and his telephone number is (612) 555-2005. Insert an *X* in the *Please Comment* check box and indicate that the fax contains 11 pages.
2. Save the fax document with the name **1-WBFax**.
3. Print and then close the document.

Assessment 4   Finding Information on Changing Grammar Checking Options

1. Open **FCTNorwayTour.docx** and then save it with the name **1-FCTNorwayTour**.
2. Use the Help feature to learn how to show readability statistics and read information on understanding readability statistics (including the *Flesch* Reading Ease score and *Flesch-Kincaid* Grade Level score). After reading the information, display the Word Options dialog box (click the File tab and then click *Options*) with the *Proofing* option selected and then insert a check mark in the *Show readability statistics* check box.
3. Complete a spelling and grammar check on the document. (*Myrdal* and *Flesch* are spelled correctly.)
4. When the readability statistics display, make a note of the word count, the *Flesch* Reading Ease score and the *Flesch-Kincaid* Grade Level score. Type that information in the appropriate locations in **1-FCTNorwayTour.docx**.
5. Display the Word Options dialog box with the *Proofing* option selected, remove the check mark from the *Show readability statistics* check box, and then close the Word Options dialog box.
6. Save, print, and then close **1-FCTNorwayTour.docx**.

Assessment 5   Creating a Certificate

1. Display the New backstage area and then search for and download the Membership certificate template (If the Membership certificate template is not available, choose a similar certificate.)
2. Identify yourself as a member in good standing in the First Choice Travel Advantage Program.
3. Save the completed document and name it **1-Membership**.
4. Print and then close the document.

Marquee Challenge

Challenge 1   Preparing a Business Letter

1. Open **MPLtrhd.docx** and then save it with the name **1-MPLtrtoWB**.
2. Create the letter shown in Figure WB-1.2. (When you type the email address in the last paragraph and then press the spacebar, Word automatically converts it to a hyperlink [blue underlined text]. (To remove the hyperlink formatting, immediately click the Undo button.) Type your initials in place of the *XX* reference initials that displays toward the end of the document.)
3. Save, print, and then close **1-MPLtrtoWB.docx**.

Challenge 2   Editing and Formatting a Travel Document

1. Open **FCTRenoTahoeVac.docx** and then save it with the name **1-FCTRenoTahoeVac**.
2. Edit and format the document so it displays as shown in Figure WB-1.3 on page WB-8. (Search for all occurrences of *Eldorado* and replace with *Sierra*. Expand the Find and Replace dialog box, insert a check mark in the *Match case* check box, and then search for all occurrences of *LT* and replace with *Lake Tahoe*. Complete a spelling and grammar check on the document.)
3. Save, print, and then close **1-FCTRenoTahoeVac.docx**.

Figure WB-1.2 Challenge 1

(Current date) *(press Enter three times)*

Ms. Dana Hirsch *(press Shift + Enter)*
The Waterfront Bistro *(press Shift + Enter)*
3104 Rivermist Drive *(press Shift + Enter)*
Buffalo, NY 14280 *(press Enter)*

Dear Ms. Hirsch: *(press Enter)*

We will be filming a movie in and around Toronto and Buffalo from July 18 to August 31, 2018. During that time, we will require catering services for cast and crew members. The services we request include breakfast, mid-morning snack, lunch, and afternoon snack for each day of filming, including weekends. *(press Enter)*

Please send information on your breakfast and lunch catering menus and snack choices. We are interested in pricing for meals and snacks for approximately 45 people for the duration of the filming. If you have any questions about our catering needs, please contact me by telephone at (612) 555-2005 or email me at JoshH@emcp.net. *(press Enter)*

Sincerely, *(press Enter two times)*

Josh Hart *(press Shift + Enter)*
Locations Director *(press Enter)*

XX *(press Shift + Enter)*
1-MPLtrtoWB.docx

955 South Alameda Street • Los Angeles, CA 90037
P: 612.555.2005 • F: 612.555.2009 • info@emcp.net • emcp.net/marquee

VACATIONING IN RENO AND LAKE TAHOE

Reno and Lake Tahoe are home to more snow, more ski resorts, and more nightlife than any other ski destination in North America. Come visit our area and experience a vast diversity of ski terrain, scenic beauty, and entertainment options. Getting to Reno and Lake Tahoe is as easy as taking one of over 250 flights that arrive daily at the Reno/Tahoe International Airport. Getting to your accommodations can be as quick as a ten-minute shuttle ride to a hotel casino in Reno or less than a scenic hour through the Sierra foothills to a variety of Lake Tahoe properties. All of the ski slopes are between 45 and 90 minutes from the Reno Airport. Getting around is easy with a variety of transportation options.

Destinations

Convenience and great locations make Incline Village and Crystal Bay desirable destinations at Lake Tahoe. Situated between Squaw Valley and Heavenly ski resorts, the two villages, along with other great resorts such as Mt. Rose and Diamond Peak, are just minutes away. Just 30 miles from Reno/Tahoe International Airport, the villages are central to all of the Lake Tahoe ski resorts. Diamond Peak offers 2,000 acres of classic Nordic terrain, over 35 kilometers of groomed tracks and skating lanes with incredible views of Lake Tahoe. The resort also boasts a 6.2-million-dollar complex including an eight-lane indoor swimming pool, cardiovascular and strength-training center, aerobic studio, and gym. Additional recreational offerings include sledding, sleigh rides, snowshoeing, bowling, and a movie theater.

North Lake Tahoe is a favored destination for discriminating vacationers. Visit this beautiful area for the epic powder, seven resorts, downhill and cross-country skiing, and unlimited dining choices—all for affordable prices. Consider trying ice skating at the world's highest ice rink, snowmobiling and snowshoeing in the backcountry, or touring Lake Tahoe on an authentic paddle-wheeler. Visit one of 80 restaurants boasting award-winning cuisine in lakeshore and alpine settings. Visit the historic town of Truckee, an old railroad and logging community with quaint shops and sights.

Lake Tahoe South Shore is the ideal destination for variety with an amazing selection of skiing for all skill levels. Almost endless lodging possibilities await you with over 95 luxurious hotels and casinos, all-suite resorts, motels, condominiums, cabins, and homes. Tour the Sierra backcountry on a snowmobile, take a paddle-wheeler cruise to Emerald Bay, try a peaceful sleigh ride, or see the sights from a dogsled.

> **Study Tools**

Study tools include a presentation and In Brief step lists. Use these resources to help you further develop and review skills learned in this section.

> **Knowledge Check**

SNAP Check your understanding by identifying application tools used in this section. If you are a SNAP user, launch the Knowledge Check from your Assignments page.

> **Recheck**

SNAP Check your understanding by taking this quiz. If you are a SNAP user, launch the Recheck from your Assignments page.

Skills Exercise

SNAP Additional activities are available to SNAP users. If you are a SNAP user, access these activities from your Assignments page.

Skills Review

> **Data File**

Review 1   Applying Character Formatting to a Travel Document

1. Open **FCTPetersburg.docx** and then save it with the name **2-FCTPetersburg**.
2. Select the entire document, change the font to Cambria, the font size to 11 points, and the font color to Blue, Accent 5, Darker 50% (ninth column, bottom row in the *Theme Colors* section).
3. Set the title *PETERSBURG, ALASKA* in 16-point Corbel.
4. Set the heading *Services* in 14-point Corbel bold and then use Format Painter to apply the same formatting to the remaining headings (*Visitor Attractions*, *Walking Tours*, *Accommodations*, and *Transportation*).
5. Use the Font dialog box to apply small caps formatting to the last sentence in the document (the sentence that begins *If you would like more*).
6. Apply the Gradient Fill - Blue, Accent 5, Reflection text effect (second column, second row) to the title *PETERSBURG, ALASKA* and then apply bold formatting.
7. Save **2-FCTPetersburg.docx**.

Review 2   Applying Paragraph Formatting to a Travel Document

1. With **2-FCTPetersburg.docx** open, center the title *PETERSBURG, ALASKA*.
2. Justify the paragraph of text below the title *PETERSBURG, ALASKA*.
3. Center the last sentence in the document (the sentence that begins *IF YOU WOULD LIKE*).
4. Justify the two paragraphs of text below the *Services* heading and indent the text 0.5 inch from the left. (Apply the formatting to the blank lines following the paragraphs as well as the paragraphs.) Use Format Painter to apply the same formatting to the four paragraphs below the *Visitor Attractions* heading, the one paragraph below the *Walking Tours* heading, the two paragraphs below the *Accommodations* heading, and the two paragraphs below the *Transportation* heading.
5. Move the insertion point to the end of the document, press the Enter key two times, and then change the paragraph alignment to right alignment.
6. Type Melissa Gehring, press Shift + Enter, and then type First Choice Travel.
7. Select the entire document, change the line spacing to 1.15, and then deselect the document.
8. Click anywhere in the *Services* heading and then change the spacing after the paragraph to 6 points.
9. Use the Repeat command (F4) to insert 6 points of spacing after the remaining headings (*Visitor Attractions*, *Walking Tours*, *Accommodations*, and *Transportation*).
10. Save, print, and then close **2-FCTPetersburg.docx**.

Review 3   Applying Indent Formatting and Finding and Replacing Formatting in a Vacation Packages Document

Data File

1. Open **FCTVacPackages.docx** and then save it with the name **2-FCTVacPackages**.
2. Select the entire document and then change the line spacing to 1.0.
3. Select the four paragraphs of text below *Fast Facts* in the *OREGON* section, click the Decrease Indent button in the Paragraph group on the Home tab to remove the indent, and then insert bullets.
4. Select the four paragraphs of text below *Fast Facts* in the *NEVADA* section, click the Decrease Indent button to remove the indent, and then insert bullets.
5. Use the Find and Replace dialog box to search for all occurrences of text set in 11-point Calibri italic and replace them with 12-point Corbel bold italic.
6. Move the insertion point to the end of the document and then type the text shown in Figure WB-2.1. ***Hint: Insert the é, è, and ñ symbols with options at the Symbol dialog box with the Symbols tab selected and the* (normal text) *font selected***.
7. Save **2-FCTVacPackages.docx**.

Figure WB-2.1 Review 3, Step 6

> Additional accommodations are available at the Ste. Thérèse Chateau and Silver Creek Resort. For information, please contact Carlos Nuñez.

1. With **2-FCTVacPackages.docx** open, move the insertion point to the blank line below the heading *Rates and Packages* in the *OREGON* section and then set a left tab at the 1-inch mark on the horizontal ruler, a center tab at the 3.5-inch mark on the horizontal ruler, and a right tab at the 5.5-inch mark on the horizontal ruler.
2. Type the three bold column headings shown in Figure WB-2.2 (*Accommodations*, *No. Persons*, *Daily Price*).
3. Type the tabbed text shown in Figure WB-2.2.
4. Move the insertion point to the blank line below the heading *Rates and Packages* in the *NEVADA* section and then set a left tab at the 1-inch mark on the horizontal ruler, a center tab at the 3.5-inch mark on the horizontal ruler, and a right tab at the 5.5-inch mark on the horizontal ruler.
5. Type the three bold column headings shown in Figure WB-2.3 (*Package*, *Length*, and *Price*) and then press the Enter key.
6. Display the Tabs dialog box, add dot leaders to the tab set at the 3.5-inch mark and the tab set at the 5.5-inch mark, and then close the dialog box.
7. Type the text in columns below the headings as shown in Figure WB-2.3.
8. Save **2-FCTVacPackages.docx**.

Figure WB-2.2 Review 4, Steps 2–3

Accommodations	No. Persons	Daily Price
Studio/one bedroom	2 to 4	$75 to $125
Two bedrooms	4 to 6	$95 to $225
Three bedrooms	6 to 8	$135 to $300
Four bedrooms	8 to 12	$160 to $400
Five/six bedrooms	10 to 16	$250 to $500

Figure WB-2.3 Review 4, Steps 5 and 7

Package	Length	Price
Tuck 'n' Roll	3 days/2 nights	$269
Ski Sneak	4 days/3 nights	$409
Take a Break	6 days/5 nights	$649
Ultimate	8 days/7 nights	$1,009

 **Review 5** Applying Borders, Shading, Styles and Themes to a Vacation Packages Document

1. With **2-FCTVacPackages.docx** open, apply the Heading 1 style to the *OREGON* title and the *NEVADA* title.
2. Apply the Heading 2 style to the headings *Fast Facts* and *Rates and Packages* in the *OREGON* section and the *NEVADA* section.

3. Insert a bottom single-line border below the *OREGON* title and below the *NEVADA* title.
4. Apply a page border with the 3-D setting, the Blue, Accent 5, Darker 25% (ninth column, fifth row) color, and a 3-point width.
5. Apply the Basic (Simple) style set.
6. Apply the Frame theme.
7. Apply the Open paragraph spacing.
8. Select the tabbed text below the *Rates and Packages* heading in the *OREGON* section and apply Teal, Accent 5, Lighter 80% paragraph shading (ninth column, second row).
9. Select the tabbed text below the *Rates and Packages* heading in the *NEVADA* section and apply Teal, Accent 5, Lighter 80% paragraph shading.
10. Save, print, and then close **2-FCTVacPackages.docx.**

Skills Assessment

Assessment 1   Formatting a Cross-Country Skiing Document

Data File

1. Open **FCTLakeTahoeSkiing.docx** and then save it with the name **2-FCTLakeTahoeSkiing**.
2. Make the following changes to the document:
   a. Set the entire document in 12-point Constantia.
   b. Set the title in 14-point Calibri bold.
   c. Set the names of the cross-country skiing resorts in 14-point Calibri bold.
   d. Change the line spacing for the entire document to 1.3.
   e. Change the paragraph spacing after the title to 0 points.
   f. Change the paragraph spacing after each heading to 6 points.
   g. Indent one-half inch from the left margin and change the alignment to justify alignment for the paragraph of text below each cross-country skiing resort name.
   h. Center the title and apply Blue, Accent 1, Lighter 40% paragraph shading (fifth column, fourth row).
   i. Apply Blue, Accent 1, Lighter 80% paragraph shading (fifth column, second row) and insert a single-line bottom border to each cross-country skiing resort name.
   j. Insert a shadow page border in standard dark blue color that is 3 points in width.
   k. Apply the Integral theme.
3. Save, print, and then close **2-FCTLakeTahoeSkiing.docx**.

Assessment 2   Preparing and Formatting a Letter

Data File

1. Open **MPLtrhd.docx** and then save it with the name **2-MPLtrtoNPC**.
2. You are Neva Smith-Wilder, Educational Liaison for Marquee Productions. Write a letter using the date April 16, 2018, to Cal Rubine, Chair, Theatre Arts Division, Niagara Peninsula College, 2199 Victoria Street, Niagara-on-the-Lake, ON L0S 1J0 and include the following information:
   • Marquee Productions will be filming in and around the city of Toronto during the summer of 2018.

- Marquee Productions would like to use approximately 20 interns to assist with the shoot.
- Interns will perform a variety of tasks, including acting as extras, assisting the camera crew, working with set designers on set construction, and providing support to the production team.
- Interns can work approximately 15 to 30 hours per week and will be compensated at minimum wage.
- Close your letter by asking Mr. Rubine to screen interested students and then send approximately 20 names to you.
- If Mr. Rubine has any questions, he may contact you at (612) 555-2005 or send the names to you by email at NevaSW@emcp.net. (Word will automatically convert the email address to a hyperlink. To remove the hyperlink formatting, immediately click the Undo button.)

3. After typing the letter, apply the following formatting:
   a. Select the letter text and then change the font to Candara.
   b. Justify the paragraph(s) in the body of the letter.
4. Save, print, and then close **2-MPLtrtoNPC.docx**.

Assessment 3   Setting Leader Tabs

1. At a blank document, type the text shown in Figure WB-2.4 with the following specifications:
   a. Center, bold, and italicize the text as shown.
   b. Set the tabbed text as shown using a left tab for the first column and a right tab with leaders for the second column.
   c. After typing the text, select the entire document, change the font to Candara, and then change the spacing after paragraphs to 0 points.
2. Save the document and name it **2-WEDistSch**.
3. Print and then close **2-WEDistSch.docx**.

Figure WB-2.4 Assessment 3

WORLDWIDE ENTERPRISES

Distribution Schedule

Two by Two

United States ....May 4

Canada...June 15

Japan .... July 20

Australia/New Zealand........................... August 3

Mexico..September 21

Assessment 4 Finding Information on Controlling Page Breaks

1. Use Word's Help feature to learn how to prevent page breaks between paragraphs and how to place at least two lines of a paragraph at the top or bottom of a page to prevent a widow (last line of a paragraph by itself at the top of a page) or orphan (first line of a paragraph by itself at the bottom of a page). (Consider reviewing the tutorial *Keeping Text Together* in Activity 2.4.)
2. Create a document containing the following information:
   a. Create a title for the document.
   b. Write a paragraph discussing how to prevent page breaks between paragraphs and list the steps required to complete the task.
   c. Write a paragraph discussing how to keep selected paragraphs together on a single page and list the steps required to complete the task.
   d. Write a paragraph discussing how to prevent a widow or orphan on a page in a document and list the steps required to complete the task.
3. Apply formatting to enhance the appearance of the document.
4. Save the completed document with the name **2-PageBreaks**.
5. Print and then close **2-PageBreaks.docx**.
6. Open **FCTVacSpecials.docx** and then save it with the name **2-FCTVacSpecials**.
7. Select the entire document and then change the font to 12-point Cambria.
8. Search for all occurrences of *Skye* and replace them with *Sky*.
9. Search for all occurrences of *Class* and replace them with *Category*.
10. Complete a spelling and grammar check on the document.
11. Click anywhere in the heading *Category S* (located toward the bottom of the first page) and then insert a command to keep the heading together with the next line.
12. Save the document and then print only page 2.
13. Close **2-FCTVacSpecials.docx**.

Assessment 5 Creating a Document with Tabbed Text

1. Determine a city outside of your state or province that you would like to visit. Using the Internet, identify four or more airlines that will fly from the airport nearest you to the city you would like to visit and determine the round-trip airfare.
2. Using the information you find, create a document with two tabbed columns. Set the first column as a left tab and type the name of the airline in this column. Set the second column as a right tab with leaders and type the airfare price in this column.
3. Create an appropriate heading for the tabbed text. Apply a paragraph border and/or shading to enhance the appearance of the tabbed text.
4. Apply a page border to the document.
5. Save the completed document with the name **2-Airfare**.
6. Print and then close **2-Airfare.docx**.

Marquee Challenge

Challenge 1 Editing and Formatting a Document on Juneau, Alaska

1. Open **FCTJuneau.docx** and then save it with the name **2-FCTJuneau**.
2. Apply the Heading 1 style to the title and the Heading 2 style to the headings.
3. Apply the Casual style set, change the theme colors to Green, change the theme fonts to Franklin Gothic, and apply the Open paragraph spacing. (Make these changes with buttons on the Design tab.)
4. Apply paragraph formatting and make changes so your document appears as shown in Figure WB-2.5.
5. Save, print, and then close **2-FCTJuneau.docx**.

Challenge 2 Creating and Formatting a Flier about a Skiing Vacation Package

1. Create the document shown in Figure WB-2.6. Apply the Cambria font, 1.5 line spacing, and page, border, shading, and bullet formatting as shown in the figure.
2. Save the completed document with the name **2-FCTSkiTahoe**.
3. Print and then close **2-FCTSkiTahoe.docx**.

JUNEAU, ALASKA

Juneau, Alaska's capital since 1900, sits at the base of Mt. Juneau. This capital blends its history as a mining town containing old storefronts and saloons with the modern architecture of government and Native corporations.

History

In the late 1800s, gold became the foundation of Juneau. The town contained a variety of gold mines with the Alaska-Juneau, or A-J, mine the most successful. The A-J mine buildings are still visible above town. Other gold mines include the Treadwill Mine complex at Douglas and the Alaska-Gastineau mine south of town. A massive cave-in occurred at Treadwill in 1917 and the mine closed. When gold content dropped below profitable margins in 1921, the Alaska-Gastineau mine closed. The A-J mine continued operations until World War II, when labor shortages and high costs forced its closure.

Visitor Attractions

Walking, hiking, and biking trails abound in and around the Juneau area. Scenic flights take visitors over the spectacular ice fields and the Glacier Bay National Monument. Take an exciting boat ride along Juneau's wilderness waterways. Tour buses take visitors to Mendanhall Glacier where they can climb moraines left by receding glaciers, hike nearby trails, and visit the U.S. Forest Service observatory where guides and exhibits explain glacier features. Visitors also can reach the glacier by driving or taking a charter flight.

Reminders of Juneau's past abound in the city. The Davis Log Cabin, built in 1881, was the community's first church and is now the visitor information center. Consider a visit to the St. Nicholas Russian Orthodox Church, which was built in 1894 and is considered the oldest original Orthodox Church in Southeast Alaska. Other city attractions include the Juneau Douglas City Museum, the pioneer cemetery, and the Wickersham House.

Museums

Juneau is the proud home to the Alaska State Museum, featuring permanent displays of Eskimo and Southeast Indian artifacts. The museum also offers changing displays of Alaska's political and natural history.

Visit the Juneau Douglas City Museum and learn about Juneau's history. Exhibits include features on gold mining and Juneau's historic past. A small admission fee is charged to adults. Children under the age of 18 are admitted free of charge.

The Alaska Maritime Heritage Foundation, a nonprofit group, is planning to build a tall ship for Alaska. It will be used to train sailors and people with disabilities in seamanship, environmental studies, goodwill trips, and charter work.

Figure WB-2.6 Challenge 2

Ski Lake Tahoe

Super Value Ski Package®

Our exciting new Super Value Ski Package features special rates on a full line of top-quality resort and hotel rentals for three days or more. Ask for the Super Value Ski Package and receive a blizzard of valuable savings for one low, inclusive price. Whatever resort or hotel you choose, you will receive the following items for free or at a considerable discount.

- Receive one free adult day lift ticket and ski all day.
- If you would like to travel throughout the Lake Tahoe area, rent any vehicle and receive a 25% discount coupon.
- For your comfort and convenience, we will include a coupon for a free ski rack rental.
- Book a Super Value Ski Package by October 31 and receive four $25 gift certificates you can use at any of the fine dining restaurants in the area.

Accommodations

Resort	3 to 5 Nights	7+ Nights
Ambassador Inn	$699	$959
Hanover's at Lake Tahoe	$679	$929
Moore Creek Lodge	$629	$879
Evergreen Suites	$619	$859
St. Rémi Resort	$607	$837
Cedar Ridge Lodge	$547	$757
Mountain Lodge	$539	$729
River Creek Resort	$525	$715

Study Tools

Study tools include a presentation and In Brief step lists. Use these resources to help you further develop and review skills learned in this section.

Knowledge Check

SNAP Check your understanding by identifying application tools used in this section. If you are a SNAP user, launch the Knowledge Check from your Assignments page.

Recheck

SNAP Check your understanding by taking this quiz. If you are a SNAP user, launch the Recheck from your Assignments page.

Skills Exercise

SNAP Additional activities are available to SNAP users. If you are a SNAP user, access these activities from your Assignments page.

Skills Review

Review 1   Copying and Pasting Text Between Travel Documents

Data Files

1. Open **FCTJuneauAK.docx** and then save it with the name **3-FCTJuneauAK**.
2. Select the entire document, click the *No Spacing* style in the Styles group, and then deselect the text.
3. Open **FCTJuneauInfo.docx**.
4. Display the Clipboard task pane and then make sure it is empty.
5. Select and then copy the text from the heading *Visitor Services* through the two paragraphs below the heading and the blank line below the two paragraphs.
6. Select and then copy the text from the heading *Transportation* through the paragraph below the heading and the blank line below the paragraph.
7. Select and then copy the text from the heading *Points of Interest* through the columns below the heading and the blank line below them.
8. Make **3-FCTJuneauAK.docx** the active document.
9. Display the Clipboard task pane.
10. Move the insertion point to the end of the document and then paste the text that begins with the heading *Points of Interest*.
11. Move the insertion point to the beginning of the heading *Points of Interest* and then paste the text that begins with the heading *Visitor Services*.

12. Move the insertion point to the beginning of the heading *Museums* and then paste the text that begins with the heading *Transportation*.
13. Clear the contents of the Clipboard task pane and then close the task pane.
14. Make **FCTJuneauInfo.docx** the active document and then close it.
15. Save **3-FCTJuneauAK.docx**.

FIRST CHOICE TRAVEL — Review 2   Moving and Formatting Text in a Travel Document

1. With **3-FCTJuneauAK.docx** open, select the heading *Visitor Centers*, the three paragraphs of text below it, and the blank line below them, and then move the selected text before the heading *Visitor Attractions*.
2. Select the heading *Museums*, the three paragraphs of text below it, and the blank line below the three paragraphs, and then move the selected text before the heading *Visitor Attractions*.
3. Change the top and bottom margins to 1.25 inches and the left and right margins to 1 inch.
4. Apply the Heading 1 style to the title *JUNEAU, ALASKA* and apply the Heading 2 style to the headings in the document (*History*, *Visitor Centers*, *Museums*, *Visitor Attractions*, *Transportation*, *Visitor Services*, and *Points of Interest*).
5. Apply the Lines (Stylish) style set, apply the Banded theme, and change the colors to *Blue II*.
6. Insert the Plain Number 3 page numbering style that inserts the page number in the upper right corner of each page.
7. Insert the SAMPLE 1 watermark.
8. Save, print, and then close **3-FCTJuneauAK.docx**.

Performance Threads — Review 3   Formatting a Report in MLA Style

Data File

1. Open **PTRenaissanceRpt.docx** and then save it with the name **3-PTRenaissanceRpt**.
2. Select the entire document, change the font to 12-point Cambria, change the line spacing to double line spacing, and then remove the spacing after paragraphs.
3. Move the insertion point to the beginning of the document, type your name, press the Enter key, type your instructor's name, press the Enter key, type the title of your course, press the Enter key, and then type the current date.
4. Insert a header that displays your last name and the page number at the right margin and changes the font to 12-point Cambria. (For help, refer to Steps 11–15 in Activity 3.7.)
5. Make sure MLA style is selected in the Citations & Bibliography group on the References tab.
6. Position the insertion point after the word *century* (but before the period) in the last sentence of the first paragraph and then insert the source information from a journal article using the following information:
   Author = Marcus Gerard
   Title = History of the Renaissance Period
   Journal Name = European History: Early Modern Europe
   Year = 2018
   Pages = 13-17

7. Position the insertion point after the text *1494* (but before the period) in the first sentence in the third paragraph and then insert the source information from a book using the following information:

Author = Iris Brooke
Title = A History of Renaissance Costumes
Year = 2017
City = New York
Publisher = Hudson River Publishing House

8. Insert a works cited page as a new page at the end of the document.
9. Edit the Gerard source so the journal name displays as *European History: Western European Civilization*.
10. Update the works cited page.
11. Format the works cited page to MLA standards by making the following changes (for help, refer to Steps 10–13 in Activity 3.8):
    a. Select the *Works Cited* heading and all entries, click the *No Spacing* style, change the font to 12-point Cambria, and change the line spacing to double line spacing.
    b. Center the title *Works Cited*.
    c. Hang-indent the entries.
12. Save, print, and then close **3-PTRenaissanceRpt.docx**.

Data File

Review 4   Preparing and Formatting an Announcement

1. At a blank document, use the Click and Type feature to type the text shown in Figure WB-3.1. *Hint: Press Shift + Enter after typing* **Sponsored by.**
2. Select the centered text you just typed and then change the font to 14-point Candara bold.
3. Select the right-aligned text you just typed and then change the font to 10-point Candara bold.
4. Change the vertical alignment of the text on the page to center alignment.
5. Save the document and name it **3-MPEmpOpps01**.
6. Print **3-MPEmpOpps01.docx**.
7. Save the document with the name **3-MPEmpOpps02**.
8. Change the vertical alignment of the text on the page back to top alignment.
9. Using the Online Pictures button, insert an image from the Internet related to movies. You determine the image as well as its size and position.
10. Delete the text *Marquee Productions* from the document and then use the Pictures button to insert the Marquee Productions logo image **MPLogo.jpg** below the text *Sponsored by*. Adjust the size and position of the image so it displays below *Sponsored by* and is approximately 0.9 inches wide.
11. Save, print, and then close **3-MPEmpOpps02.docx**.

> EMPLOYMENT OPPORTUNITIES
>
> Working in the Movie Industry
>
> Wednesday, March 14, 2018
>
> 7:00 to 8:30 p.m.
>
> Sponsored by
> Marquee Productions

Review 5 Preparing an Envelope

1. At a blank document, prepare an envelope with the return address and delivery address shown below. (Type your name below *First Choice Travel* in the return address.) Add the envelope to the document.

Delivery address:

Chris Greenbaum
Marquee Productions
955 South Alameda Street
Los Angeles, CA 90037

Return address:

First Choice Travel
Student Name
3588 Ventura Boulevard
Los Angeles, CA 90102

2. Save the document and name it **3-FCTEnv**.
3. Print and then close **3-FCTEnv.docx**. (Manual feed of the envelope may be required.)

Review 6 Preparing Mailing Labels

1. At a blank document, prepare a sheet of mailing labels for the following name and address using the Avery US Letter vendor and 5160 Easy Peel Address Labels product number. (Type your name below *Worldwide Enterprises*.)

Worldwide Enterprises
Student Name
1112-1583 Broadway
New York, NY 10110

2. Save the mailing label document and name it **3-WELabels**.
3. Print and then close **3-WELabels.docx**.

Skills Assessment

Assessment 1 Formatting a Costume Rental Agreement

Data File

1. Open **PTAgreement.docx** and then save it with the name **3-PTAgreement**.
2. Search for all occurrences of *Customer* and replace them with *Marquee Productions*.
3. Move the *4. Alterations* section above the *3. Marquee Productions Agrees* section and then renumber the two sections.

4. Select the entire document, change the font to 12-point Constantia, and then deselect the document.
5. Change the top margin to 1.5 inches.
6. Insert the Semaphore footer.
7. Save, print, and then close **3-PTAgreement.docx**.

Assessment 2 Creating an Announcement

1. At a blank document, create an announcement for Niagara Peninsula College by typing the text shown in Figure WB-3.2.
2. Change the font for the entire document to a decorative font, size, and color of your choosing.
3. Change the line spacing to double line spacing for the entire document.
4. Insert, size, and move an online image of your choosing related to the subject of the announcement.
5. Save the document and name it **3-NPCInternship**.
6. Print and then close **3-NPCInternship.docx**.

Figure WB-3.2 Assessment 2

NIAGARA PENINSULA COLLEGE

Internship Opportunities

June 18 through August 31, 2018

Marquee Productions, Toronto Office

Contact Cal Rubine, Theatre Arts Division

Assessment 3 Preparing Mailing Labels

1. Prepare return mailing labels with the following information. (Type your name below *Niagara Peninsula College*.)

   Niagara Peninsula College
   Student Name
   2199 Victoria Street
   Niagara-on-the-Lake, ON L0S 1J0

2. Save the labels document and name it **3-NPCLabels**.
3. Print and then close **3-NPCLabels.docx**.

Assessment 4 Finding Information on Creating a Picture Watermark

1. Open **3-MPEmpOpps01.docx** and save it with the name **3-MPEmpOpps-Wtrmark**.
2. Use Word's Help feature to learn how to insert a picture watermark.
3. Insert **MPLogo.jpg**, as a watermark.
4. Save, print, and then close **3-MPEmpOpps-Wtrmark.docx**.

Assessment 5   Creating a Personal Letterhead

1. At a blank document, create a letterhead that includes your first and last names, address, and telephone number, and insert an image in the letterhead that represents you or something in which you are interested. Apply font formatting to the text in the letterhead and size and position the image. (For letterhead examples, refer to **FCTLtrhd.docx** and **MPLtrhd.docx**. The letterheads in these two documents were created as headers. If you want to create your letterhead in a header, click the Insert tab, click the Header button in the Header & Footer group and then click *Edit Header*.)
2. Save the document and name it **3-Ltrhd**.
3. Print and then close **3-Ltrhd.docx**.

Marquee Challenge

Performance Threads   **Challenge 1**   Formatting a Costume Document

1. Open **PTCostumes.docx** and then save it with the name **3-PTCostumes**.
2. Format your document so it displays similar to the document in Figure WB-3.3 on pages WB-25–WB-26. To do this, apply the following formatting:
   - Change the top margin to *1.25"*.
   - Insert, size, and position **PTLogo.jpg** as shown. *Hint: Change the position to* **Position in Top Center with Square Text Wrapping** *and then change the text wrapping to* **Top and Bottom.**
   - Apply the Heading 1 style to the headings.
   - Apply the Lines (Simple) style set.
   - Apply the Ion theme and then apply the Candara theme font. (Use the Fonts button on the Design tab.)
   - Apply bold and italic formatting to the headings.
   - Apply White, Background 1, Darker 5% paragraph shading to the headings (first column, second row).
   - Insert the page border (the tenth page border option from the end of the *Art* option drop-down list) and then change the width to 6 points and the color to standard dark red (in the *Standard Colors* section).
   - Change the paragraph alignment and insert numbers and bullets as shown.
   - Insert **Books.png**. Change the image color to Dark Red, Accent color 1 Light (second column, third row in the *Recolor* section), the correction to Brightness: +40% Contrast: +40% (last option in the *Brightness/Contrast* section) and then size and position the image as shown.
3. Save, print, and then close **3-PTCostumes.docx**.

 Worldwide Enterprises   **Challenge 2**   Preparing an Announcement

1. At a blank document, create the document shown in Figure WB-3.4 on page WB-27 with the following specifications:
   - Apply the No Spacing style.
   - Change the line spacing to 1.5 lines and change the font size to 16 points.
   - Change to landscape orientation.
   - Press the Enter key three times and then type the text in the document. When typing the text, press the Enter key after typing the title and press Shift + Enter to end each remaining line of text. *Note: Do not press the Enter key or Shift + Enter after the last line.*

- Apply the page border and insert the page background color as shown in the figure.
- Insert **WELogo.jpg**. Change the white background of the logo image to transparent by clicking the Color button on the Picture Tools Format tab, clicking the *Set Transparent Color* option, and then clicking in a white area inside the logo image. Size and position the image as shown in the figure.
- Insert **Businesspeople.png**. Set the white background of the image to transparent color. Size and position the image as shown in the figure.
- Insert the watermark as shown.
2. Save the document and name it **3-WENotice**.
3. Print and then close **3-WENotice.docx**.

Figure WB-3.3 Challenge 1

Performance Threads

Renaissance Period

The Renaissance period was a series of cultural and literary movements that took place in the fourteenth, fifteenth, and sixteenth centuries in Europe. The word *renaissance* means "rebirth" and originated with the belief that Europeans had rediscovered the intellectual and cultural superiority of the Greek and Roman cultures. The Renaissance period was preceded by the Middle Ages, also known as the "Dark Ages," which began with the collapse of the Roman Empire in the fifth century. The term *renaissance* was coined by Jacob Burckhardt in the eighteenth century in *The Civilization of the Renaissance in Italy*.

Renaissance education was designed to produce a person well-versed in humanities, mathematics, science, sports, and art. The Renaissance person had extensive knowledge in many fields, explored beyond the boundaries of learning and geographical knowledge, and embraced free thought and skepticism. Artists, writers, explorers, architects, and scientists were motivated by a revival in classical Greek and Roman culture and a return to classical values. During the Middle Ages, interest in culture and learning was primarily confined to theologians, philosophers, and writers. During the Renaissance period, however, people from all social, political, and economic classes involved themselves in the study of classical literature and art.

Renaissance Costume

Renaissance costume developed in Italy and was introduced to Western Europe following the invasion of Italy by Charles VIII of France in 1494. Due to the warmer climate in Italy, simpler styles evolved independently from the rest of Europe. Men's clothing consisted of low-necked tunics and chemises and women's clothing consisted of simple and low-necked gowns called "Juliet" gowns. During the middle of the fifteenth century, clothing assumed a more natural appearance. Women wore dresses with attached bodices and skirts. Men's doublets became shorter and hosiery became more prominent. Interest by women in gothic headdresses declined and instead they trimmed their hair with veils, ribbons, and jewels. Lace and perfume became more prevalent during the Renaissance period.

Early in the Renaissance period, women's dress included a long, rigid, cone-shaped corset reaching below the waist to a "V" in the front. Women's gowns expanded below the waistline and by the middle sixteenth century were supported by hoops made of wire that were held together with ribbons. This hoop skirt, called a *farthingale*, reached its maximum width around the early seventeenth century and then changed to a cartwheel or drum shape. Ballooned sleeves and circular lace collars also typified the early seventeenth century costume. Men's clothing had a similar look with puffed-out hose, balloon sleeves, padded doublets, and large ruff collars.

continues

Figure WB-3.3 Challenge 1—*continued*

Costume Vocabulary

1. Basquine: A very large skirt that was open and stretched on circles.
2. Berne: A very large, fixed, and pleated scarf that rested on the shoulder.
3. Jupon: Long-sleeved camisole generally worn by men and women in Spain.
4. Mantilla: A kind of shawl worn by women to cover the head and shoulders.
5. Marlotte: A coat with pleats in the back and short, curved sleeves.

Costume Books

- Arnold, Janet, *Patterns of Fashion*
- Barton, Lucy, *Historic Costume for the Stage*
- Boucher, Francois, *20,000 Years of Fashion*
- Brooke, Iris, *A History of Costume*
- Evans, Mary, *Costume Throughout the Ages*
- LaMar, Virginia A., *English Dress in the Age of Shakespeare*

Figure WB-3.4 Challenge 2

Worldwide Enterprises

IMPORTANT NOTICE!!

We need additional employees to work the next two weekends to complete a special distribution order. If you are interested in working any shift this weekend and/or next, please contact Rhonda Trask in Human Resources at extension 3360. We are offering overtime pay plus a bonus based on your hourly or salaried wage.

Study Tools

Study tools include a presentation and In Brief step lists. Use these resources to help you further develop and review skills learned in this section.

Knowledge Check

SNAP Check your understanding by identifying application tools used in this section. If you are a SNAP user, launch the Knowledge Check from your Assignments page.

Recheck

SNAP Check your understanding by taking this quiz. If you are a SNAP user, launch the Recheck from your Assignments page.

Skills Exercise

SNAP Additional activities are available to SNAP users. If you are a SNAP user, access these activities from your Assignments page.

Skills Review

Data Files

Review 1 Formatting a Travel Document

1. Open **FCTZenithAdv.docx** and then save it with the name **4-FCTZenithAdv**.
2. Move the insertion point to the beginning of the heading *Upcoming Adventures* and then insert **FCTBicyclingAdv.docx**. ***Hint: Do this with the Object button on the Insert tab.***
3. Position the insertion point in the top cell in the first column in the table in the *Bicycling Adventures* section and then change the width to 1.7 inches. ***Hint: Do this with the* Table Column Width *measurement box in the Cell Size group on the Table Tools Layout tab.***
4. Position the insertion point in the top cell in the middle column and then change the width to 0.7 inch.
5. Position the insertion point in the top cell in the last column and then change the width to 0.7 inch.
6. With the insertion point positioned in any cell in the table in the *Bicycling Adventures* section, apply the Grid Table 4 - Accent 1 table style (second column, fourth row in the *Grid Tables* section), and then click the *First Column* check box in the Table Style Options group on the Table Tools Design tab to remove the check mark.
7. Apply the same table style (remove the check mark from the *First Column* check box) to the other two tables in the document.

8. Select the heading *Antarctic Zenith Adventures* and then apply the Intense Reference style. ***Hint: Click the More Styles button in the Styles group on the Home tab to display this style.***

9. Apply the Intense Reference style to the remaining three headings in the document.

10. Use the Colors button on the Design tab to apply the Red color theme.

11. Use the Fonts button on the Design tab to apply the Arial-Times New Roman font theme.

12. Save **4-FCTZenithAdv.docx**.

 **Review 2** Inserting Objects and Applying Column Formatting in a Travel Document

1. With **4-FCTZenithAdv.docx** open, move the insertion point to the beginning of the document and then insert WordArt with the following specifications:

   a. Click the *Fill - Dark Red, Accent 1, Shadow* option at the WordArt button drop-down list (second column, first row).

   b. Type Zenith Adventures as the WordArt text.

   c. Change the WordArt text height to 1 inch and the width to 6.5 inches.

   d. Change the position of the WordArt to In Line with Text. (Do this with the Layout Options button at the right of the WordArt border.)

   e. Click the Text Effects button, point to *Transform*, and then click the *Can Up* option (third column, fourth row in the *Warp* section).

2. Move the insertion point to the beginning of the first paragraph in the document and then insert a continuous section break.

3. Create two newspaper columns with 0.4 inch of spacing between them.

4. Insert a text box with the following specifications:

   a. Insert the Simple Text Box predesigned text box in the document and then type the following in the text box: First Choice Travel is teaming with Zenith Adventures to provide our clients with thrilling and extreme outdoor adventures.

   b. Change the text box shape style to Colored Outline - Orange, Accent 2 (third column, first row in the *Theme Styles* section).

   c. Select the text in the text box and then change the font size to 10 points and apply bold and italic formatting.

   d. Change the height of the text box to 0.8 inch and the width to 2.1 inches.

   e. Change the position of the text box to Position in Middle Center with Square Text Wrapping.

5. Create a drop cap with the first letter of the first paragraph in the document (the letter *W* in *We*) and then change the font color for the *W* to Dark Red, Accent 1, Darker 25% (fifth column, fifth row in the *Theme Colors* section).

6. Move the insertion point to the end of the document and then insert a continuous section break (this balances the columns on the second page).

7. Press Ctrl + End to move the insertion point to the end of the document after the continuous section break and then press the Enter key.

8. Click the Layout tab, click the Columns button, and then click *One* at the drop-down list.

9. Draw and format the shape and insert text as shown in Figure WB-4.1 using the following specifications:

   a. Insert the Up Ribbon shape in the *Stars and Banners* section at the location of the insertion point.

   b. Change the height of the drawn shape to 1.5 inches and the width to 4.2 inches.

c. Use the Align button on the Drawing Tools Format tab to horizontally distribute the shape.

d. Change the shape style to Subtle Effect - Orange, Accent 2 (third column, fourth row in the *Theme Styles* section).

e. Type the text in the shape as shown in Figure WB-4.1. Apply bold and italic formatting and change the font size to 24 points.

10. Save, print, and then close **4-FCTZenithAdv.docx**.

Figure WB-4.1 Review 2, Step 9

Review 3   Creating and Formatting SmartArt

1. Open **MPProdDept.docx** and then save it with the name **4-MPProdDept**.
2. Press Ctrl + End and then create the organizational chart shown in Figure WB-4.2 with the following specifications:
   a. Display the Choose a SmartArt Graphic dialog box, click *Hierarchy* in the left panel, and then double-click the *Organization Chart* option.
   b. Select the SmartArt graphic (not a specific shape in the graphic) and then apply the Cartoon SmartArt style and change the colors to Colorful Range - Accent Colors 5 to 6.
   c. Click the SmartArt Tools Format tab and then change the height of the SmartArt graphic to 2.5 inches and the width to 5 inches. (Do this with the Size button or in the Size group.)
   d. Change the text fill color to Black, Text 1 using the Text Fill button arrow.
   e. Type the text in the boxes as shown in Figure WB-4.2. (Press Shift + Enter after typing the names.)
3. Create the graphic shown in Figure WB-4.3 with the following specifications:
   a. Press Ctrl + End to move the insertion point to the end of the document and then press the Enter key three times.
   b. Display the Choose a SmartArt Graphic dialog box, click *Process* in the left panel, and then double-click the *Continuous Block Process* option.
   c. Select the SmartArt process graphic (not a specific shape in the graphic) and then change the SmartArt style to Polished.
   d. Change the colors to Colorful Range - Accent Colors 5 to 6.
   e. Click the SmartArt Tools Format tab and then change the height to 2.5 inches and the width to 5 inches.
   f. Change the text fill color to Black, Text 1 using the Text Fill button arrow.
   g. Type the text in the boxes as shown in Figure WB-4.3.
4. Make sure the organizational chart graphic and process graphic fit on the page.
5. Save, print, and then close **4-MPProdDept.docx**.

Figure WB-4.2 Review 3 SmartArt Organizational Chart

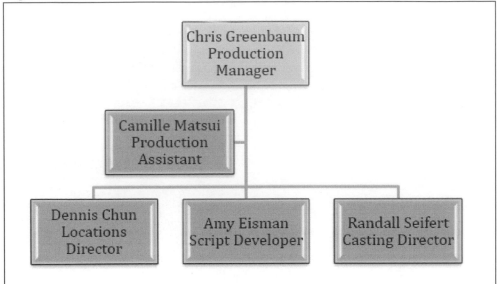

Figure WB-4.2 Review 3 SmartArt Organizational Chart

Figure WB-4.3 Review 3 SmartArt Graphic

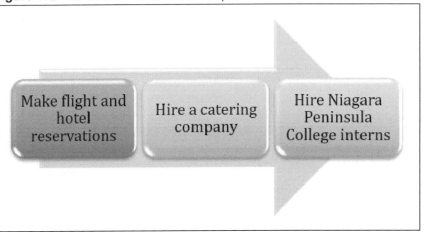

NIAGARA
PENINSULA
COLLEGE

Review 4 Preparing, Modifying, and Formatting a Table

1. At a blank document, create a table with four columns and five rows.
2. Type the text in the cells as shown in Figure WB-4.4.
3. Insert a new column at the right side of the table and then type the following text in the new cells:

   Instructor
   Crowe
   Rubine
   McAllister
   Auve

4. Change the width of each column to the following measurements:

   First column = 0.6 inch
   Second column = 1.3 inches
   Third column = 0.7 inch
   Fourth column = 1.25 inches
   Fifth column = 1 inch

5. Insert a new row above the first row and then, with the new row selected, merge the cells.
6. Type THEATRE ARTS DIVISION FALL SCHEDULE in the cell and then bold and center the text.
7. Select the second row (contains the text *Course, Name, Days*, and so on) and then bold and center the text.
8. Display the Table Tools Design tab and then remove all check marks from the check boxes in the Table Style Options group *except* the *Header Row* and *Banded Rows* check boxes.
9. Change the table style to Grid Table 5 Dark - Accent 2 (third column, fifth row in the *Grid Tables* section).
10. Select the text in the first row (*THEATRE ARTS DIVISION FALL SCHEDULE*), change the font size to 14 points, and then apply bold formatting.
11. Horizontally center the table on the page. ***Hint: Do this at the Table Properties dialog box with the Table tab selected.***
12. Save the document and name it **4-NPCFallSch**.
13. Print and then close **4-NPCFallSch.docx**.

Figure WB-4.4 Review 4

Course	Name	Days	Time
TR 101	Intro to Theatre	MTWRF	8:00-8:50 a.m.
TR 125	Beginning Acting	MTWR	9:00-9:50 a.m.
TR 211	Set Design	MTW	10:00-10:50 a.m.
TR 251	Costume Design	MW	3:00-4:20 p.m.

FIRST CHOICE
TRAVEL

Data File

Review 5   Inserting a Hyperlink; Saving a Document in PDF Format

1. Open **FCTOslo.docx** and then save it with the name **4-FCTOslo**.
2. Change the bottom margin to 0.8 inch.
3. Apply the Title style to the text *Oslo, Norway* and apply the Heading 2 style to the headings in the document (*History*; *Population*; *Commerce and Industry*; *Climate*; *Holiday, Sport, and Leisure*; and *Sightseeing Tours*).
4. Apply the Word 2010 style set.
5. Move the insertion point to the beginning of the heading *History*, insert a continuous section break, and then create two newspaper columns with a line between them.
6. Save and then print **4-FCTOslo.docx**.
7. Move the insertion point to the end of the document, press the Enter key two times, and then type Additional Information on Norway.
8. Select the text *Additional Information on Norway* and then insert a hyperlink to the official site of Norway for the United States at www.norway.org.
9. Make sure you are connected to the Internet, hold down the Ctrl key, and then click the Additional Information on Norway hyperlink.
10. At the Norway site, click any hyperlink that interests you. When you are finished, close the web browser.

11. Save the document in PDF format at the Save As dialog box.
12. After viewing the document in Adobe Acrobat Reader, close Adobe Acrobat Reader.
13. Save and then close **4-FCTOslo.docx**.

Review 6   Merging Letters and Envelopes

1. Create a data source file with the following names and addresses. (You determine the fields to delete; use the *State* field for the ON [Ontario] province and the *ZIP Code* field for the postal codes.)

Mr. Frank Tolentino
Royal Fabrics and Supplies
3220 Wilson Avenue
Toronto, ON M4C 3S3

Mrs. Anna Strassburg
Millwood Fabrics
550 Jane Street
Toronto, ON M4B 2C7

Mrs. Andrea Jones-Leigh
JL Fabrics and Crafts
1230 Sheppard Avenue
Toronto, ON M6H 4J2

Mr. Donald Enslow
Wright Fabrics and Design
8744 Huron Street
London, ON N5V 2K8

2. Save the data source file with the name **4-PTDataSource**.
3. Open **PTFabricLtr.docx** and then save it with the name **4-PTFabricLtrMD**.
4. Specify **4-PTDataSource.mdb** as the data source file.
5. Insert the *Address Block* field and the *Greeting Line* field in the appropriate locations in the letter.
6. Move the insertion point immediately right of the word *company* in the last sentence of the third paragraph, type a comma, and then press the spacebar. Insert the *Title* field, press the spacebar, insert the *Last Name* field, and then type a comma.
7. Merge all of the records into a new document.
8. Save the merged letters document and name it **4-PTMergedFabricLtrs**.
9. Print and then close the document.
10. Save and then close **4-FabricLtrMD.docx**.
11. Create an envelope document, specify **4-PTDataSource.mdb** as the data source file, and then merge the envelopes.
12. Save the merged envelopes document and name it **4-PTMergedEnvs**.
13. Print and then close the document.
14. Close the envelope main document without saving it.

Skills Assessment

Assessment 1   Formatting a Theatre Arts Division Newsletter

1. Open **NPCTheatreNewsltr.docx** and then save it with the name **4-NPCTheatreNewsltr**.
2. Move the insertion point to the end of the document and then insert the document named **NPCProductions.docx**.
3. Use the Fonts button on the Design tab to change the theme fonts to Calibri Light-Constantia and then apply the Heading 2 style to the three headings in the document.

4. Insert a continuous section break at the beginning of the *Division Description* heading and then format the text into two columns.

5. Move the insertion point to the beginning of the document and then insert the text *Theatre Arts Division* as WordArt. You determine the layout and format of the WordArt. Change the height of the WordArt to 1 inch and the width to 6.5 inches. Apply a transform effect and change the position of the WordArt to *In Line with Text*.

6. Move the insertion point to anywhere in the heading *Division Description*, insert the Simple Text Box predesigned text box, and then type the text The Niagara Peninsula College theatre experience can be the beginning of a lifelong interest in the art of theatre. Select the text in the text box, change the font size to 9 points, and then apply bold and italic formatting. Change the shape style to Subtle Effect - Blue, Accent 1 (second column, fourth row in the *Theme Styles* section), change the shape height of the text box to 0.7 inches, and then change the position of the text box to Position in Middle Center with Square Text Wrapping.

7. Move the insertion point to the end of the document and then insert a continuous section break.

8. Save, print, and then close **4-NPCTheatreNewsltr.docx**.

Performance Threads   **Assessment 2**   Creating SmartArt Graphics

1. Open **PTDesignDept.docx** and then save it with the name **4-PTDesignDept**.
2. Move the insertion point to the end of the document and then create a SmartArt organizational chart with the following information:

Camilla Yong
Design Manager

Scott Bercini   Terri Cantrell   Paul Gottlieb
Designer   Designer/Sewer   Designer/Sewer

3. Apply formatting and/or design elements to enhance the appearance of the organizational chart.

4. Move the insertion point below the organizational chart and then create a SmartArt graphic with the Converging Radial graphic in the *Relationship* group at the Choose a SmartArt Graphic dialog box that contains the following text:

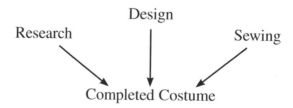

5. Apply formatting and/or design elements to enhance the appearance of the graphic. Change the text wrapping to Tight and then move the graphic below the organizational chart.

6. Make any necessary adjustments to spacing and/or size to ensure that the SmartArt organizational chart graphic and relationship graphic fit on one page.

7. Save, print, and then close **4-PTDesignDept.docx**.

Assessment 3   Creating a Table for the Waterfront Bistro

1. At a blank document, create a table with the text shown in Figure WB-4.5.
2. Apply design and layout features to enhance the appearance of the table.
3. Center the table horizontally on the page.
4. Save the document with the name **4-WBLunchOptions**.
5. Print and then close **4-WBLunchOptions.docx**.

Figure WB-4.5 Assessment 3

CATERED LUNCH OPTIONS			
Option	Contents	Cost per Person	Discount Price
Option A: Hot	Vegetarian quiche, Caesar salad, vegetables, dressing, dessert, and beverages	$11.75	$10.95
Option B: Deli	Turkey or ham sandwiches, chips, vegetables, dressing, brownies, and beverages	$9.75	$9.30
Option C: Continental	Bagels, rolls, cream cheese, vegetables, dressing, cookies, and beverages	$8.95	$8.50

Assessment 4   Finding Information on Flipping and Copying Objects

1. Use Word's Help feature to learn how to flip and copy objects, or draw a shape and then experiment with the Rotate button on the Drawing Tools Format tab.
2. At a blank document, create the document shown in Figure WB-4.6. Use the Pictures button in the Illustrations group on the Insert tab to insert **WELogo.jpg**. Create the arrow at the left with the Striped Right Arrow shape in the *Block Arrows* section. Apply the Intense Effect - Blue, Accent 1 shape style (second column, last row in the *Theme Styles* section), the Angle shape effect (first column, second row in the *Bevel* section), and the Offset Diagonal Top Left shadow shape effect (third column, third row in the *Outer* section). Copy and flip the arrow to create the arrow at the right side.
3. Save the completed document with the name **4-WEStockholderMtg**.
4. Print and then close **4-WEStockholderMtg.docx**.

Figure WB-4.6 Assessment 4

Assessment 5   Locating Information and Creating a Table

1. Using the Internet, search for information on car rentals in your area. Locate pricing information on economy and midsize cars and also minivans. Find out the daily rental fees for each, as well as the weekly rental fee.
2. At a blank document, create a table that contains the information you found on car rentals. Modify and format the table so the information is attractive and easy to read.
3. Save the document with the name **4-CarRentalInfo**.
4. Print and then close **4-CarRentalInfo.docx**.

Marquee Challenge

Challenge 1   Preparing a Flyer for The Waterfront Bistro

Data File

1. At a blank document, create the document shown in Figure WB-4.7 on page WB-38 with the following specifications:
   - Insert **TWBLogo.jpg**, change the height to 1.3 inches, and then change the position to Position in Top Left with Square Text Wrapping.
   - Set the text in the Candara font (you determine the sizes) in the standard dark blue color.
   - Insert the art page border (down approximately one-third in the *Art* drop-down list).
   - Insert the line below the logo as a border and change the color to standard dark blue.
   - Apply any other formatting required to create the document as shown in Figure WB-4.7.
2. Save the completed document with the name **4-WBFlyer**.
3. Print and then close **4-WBFlyer.docx**.

Figure WB-4.7 Challenge 1

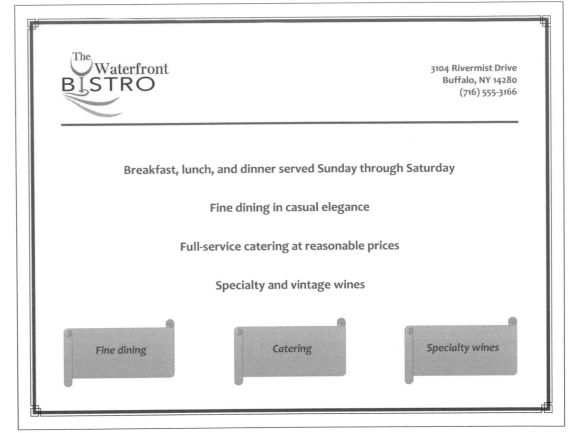

Challenge 2   Formatting a Document on Orcas Island

1. Open **FCTOrcasIsland.docx** and then save it with the name **4-FCTOrcasIsland**.
2. Format the document so it displays as shown in Figure WB-4.8, with the following specifications:
   - Use the Colors button on the Design tab to change the theme colors to Blue Green.
   - Use the Fonts button on the Design tab to change the theme fonts to Century Gothic-Palatino.
   - Apply the Heading 2 style to the headings.
   - Format the text into two columns as shown in Figure WB-4.8.
   - Create the drop cap as shown. Change the font color for the drop cap to Aqua, Accent 1, Lighter 40% (fifth column, fourth row in the *Theme Colors* section).
   - Create the WordArt with the Fill - Aqua, Accent 1, Shadow WordArt style (second column, first row), change the height to 1 inch and the width to 6.5 inches, change the position to *In Line with Text*, and apply the Can Down transform text effect (fourth column, fourth row in the *Warp* section) and the Offset Top shadow text effect (second column, third row in the *Outer* section).
   - Insert **Lighthouse.png**. Change the height of the lighthouse image to 1.9 inches and change the position to Position in Middle Center with Square Text Wrapping.
   - Balance the columns on the second page.
3. Save, print, and then close **4-FCTOrcasIsland.docx**.

Orcas Island

The San Juan Islands in Washington State include a number of islands including Orcas Island, which has long been a favorite destination for generations of vacationers. Located approximately 60 miles north of Seattle, it lies in the Strait of Georgia between Anacortes and Vancouver Island. To the north, on the mainland, is Vancouver, B.C. With its fjord-like bays and sounds, deep harbors, lakes, streams, and waterfalls, Orcas is considered the most spectacular of the islands. The island is over 56 square miles in size and has more than 125 miles of saltwater shoreline. Winding roads fan out from the business and social center of Eastsound village to the nearby communities of Deer Harbor, Orcas, and Olga. One of the greatest assets of the island is Mt. Constitution in Moran State Park, which offers panoramic views of the entire archipelago and is surrounded by miles of trails and sparkling lakes.

Activities on Orcas

Orcas Island offers an unhurried setting to enjoy the spectacular scenery and

wildlife, with a wide variety of recreation. Activities include hiking, biking, golfing, sailing, kayaking, shopping, flying, and fishing. During the summer and on weekends and holidays, several resorts and lounges offer live music. Throughout the year, Orcas Theatre and Community Center offers concerts, plays, art exhibits, dances, workshops, movies, and many special events.

Bicycling Safety

Orcas Island is the most challenging of the islands for bicyclists. This is due to the narrow, winding roads and hilly terrain. When bicycling on the island, ride single file and keep to the right side of the road. Make stops on a straight-of-way rather than at the top of a hill or on a curve. Motorists cannot negotiate blind approaches safely with a bicyclist on the road. When stopping to rest or regroup, enjoy the scenery, but please move completely off the road. As you enjoy the scenery, be alert for potential traffic and the condition of the roadway. When leaving the ferry, pull over to the side of the road and let the automobiles pass.

continues

Marine Parks
These marine parks are accessible only by boat:

- Sucia Island: Cluster of 11 islands; trails, bays, and bluffs; 2.5 miles from Orcas Island
- Patos: Two buoys, four campsites, trails (no water)
- Matis: One hundred and fifty acres, two buoys, and ten campsites

Directions to Orcas Island
You can reach Orcas Island either by ferry or by airplane. The primary departure point for the Washington State Ferry is Anacortes. To reach Anacortes, take Interstate 5 to State Highway 20 (exit 230) and travel west about 20 miles to the ferry terminal. The ferry ride lasts approximately one hour and fifteen minutes. Consider arriving at least one hour ahead of your desired departure time. Kenmore Air and West Isle Air each offer scheduled flights from Anacortes and Bellingham to Orcas Island. Flights arrive at Eastsound Airport, Rosario, or Westsound. Landings in Rosario and Westsound require float planes.